I don't want to, but I've got to...

Why was the shirt sad?

Because the jeans were BLUE!

Cool stuff I'd rather do

People to prank today

1
2
3
4

DING, DONG MERRILY!

Secretly record the sound of your front doorbell. Play it back when everyone is too busy to answer the door! ROTFL as they race to the door, only to find no one is there!

Who did you prank?	Prank rating (out of five)
	★ ★ ★ ★ ★
	★ ★ ★ ★ ★
	★ ★ ★ ★ ★

Do it!

Don't do it!

Flies to cut out and keep!

TIME TROUBLE

Have your family in a spin by turning the clocks forward!

This prank is best performed on a day when everyone's home so the joke can be enjoyed by all! Get up early (difficult but worth the trouble) and move as many clocks as you can forward by three hours. Stand back and watch the scramble when everyone thinks they are late for their important appointments!

Who did you prank?	Prank rating (out of five)
	★ ★ ★ ★ ★
	★ ★ ★ ★ ★
	★ ★ ★ ★ ★

What do you get if you put your pen in the freezer?
Iced ink?
Well, yes you do, but that wasn't the question!

CRUNCHY CUSHIONS

Take your brother's or sister's pillows from their cases and replace them with scrunched up newspaper.

Sweet dreams!

When should you never suck your food?

Chewsday!

Things to do if I find the time

Maggots to cut out and keep!

Oops! Nearly forgot!

Who did you prank?	Prank rating (out of five)
	★ ★ ★ ★ ★
	★ ★ ★ ★ ★
	★ ★ ★ ★ ★

Give sprout man a face!

Things to do
before I clean my room

People to prank today

 1

 2

 **3**

4

What did the man say when he put on a coat made of sausages?

Dinner's on me!

What do elves do after school?

Their gnomework!

PRANK CALL

When you are both in a nice, busy space (like on the playground or in a shop), move a little distance from your friend and then pretend to answer your phone. Act like you're taking a call and shout to your friend, "Hey, your mother wants to know if you want your underpants ironed!"

Who did you prank?	Prank rating (out of five)
	★ ★ ★ ★ ★
	★ ★ ★ ★ ★
	★ ★ ★ ★ ★

MAKE WHOOPEE

5 excellent uses for a whoopee cushion.

1. Slip it under the cushion of your dad's favourite chair.

2. Give it a squeeze just as everyone sits down for a nice family lunch.

3. How about ripping a parp at the dentist?

4. Or leaving it under a cushion in your sister's bedroom?

5. Punk your pal by leaving a cushion on his seat at the cinema – it's so dark, he'll never see it coming!

Who did you prank?	Prank rating (out of five)
	★ ★ ★ ★ ★
	★ ★ ★ ★ ★
	★ ★ ★ ★ ★

Cool
stuff to do

Stuff to do
(or I'll get in trouble)

Why did the broom get married so fast?

Because she was swept off her feet!

Why did the banana go to the hospital?

Because it wasn't peeling well!

Don't forget

People to prank today

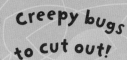

EXCUSE ME!

Why did the tomato blush?
Because he saw the salad dressing!

CEREAL SWITCH!

What could be more merry than causing mealtime mayhem at the breakfast table?

The night before you spring your surprise, sneak into the kitchen and swap the inside bags of everyone's favourite cereals.

Perfect your plan by sealing any squeeze bottles and giving them a milky surprise with food colouring!

The next morning, step back, act dumb, and let the chaos commence!

TOP 5 USES FOR PLASTIC CRITTERS

Scatter them freely in your sister's underwear drawer.

Hide one under the TV remote.

Tie to pieces of black cotton and dangle them from door frames.

Hide them in your friends' shoes.

Drop one on your sister's head when she's not looking and see how long it takes her to find it tangled in her lovely locks!

Creepy bugs to cut out!

BIG FOOT!

This prank is perfect for hot summer days.

Begin the prank by telling your victim you've read about how, in the summer, the heat makes people's feet grow bigger. Ask them if they've ever heard this, then change the subject. The next day, take a rolled-up handkerchief or sock and stuff it in the toes of your victim's shoes. Let the laughs roll in as they think their feet have ballooned!

Who did you prank?	Prank rating (out of five)
	★ ★ ★ ★ ★
	★ ★ ★ ★ ★
	★ ★ ★ ★ ★

When's the best time to chop down a tree?
Sep-timber!

How do you make a hat stand?

Take away its chair!

No way will I EVER...

People to prank today

1
2
3
4

Things I might forget...

People to prank today

1.
2.
3.
4.

WHOSE CAT DID THAT?

You will need:

- PVA glue
- clingfilm
- an old magazine
- a biscuit or cracker

Fake puke is easy to make and great for livening up a boring visit to the supermarket.

First crush the biscuit. Be sure to have a good mix of chunky bits and fine, crumbly pieces.

Place the clingfilm flat on the magazine. Squirt a blob of glue onto the clingfilm, then sprinkle the crushed biscuit on top.

Leave for at least a day, then gently peel the fake puke from the clingfilm.

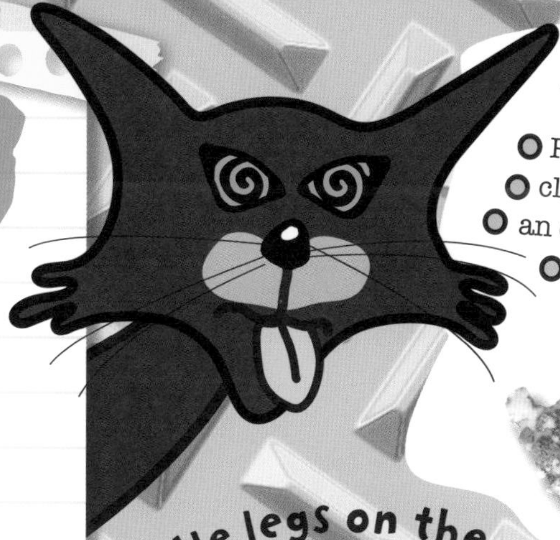

Doodle legs on the underpants!

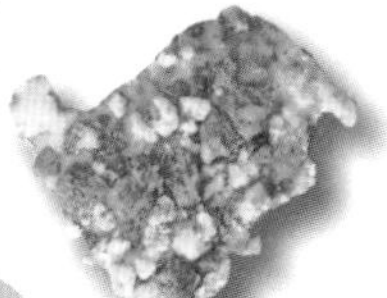

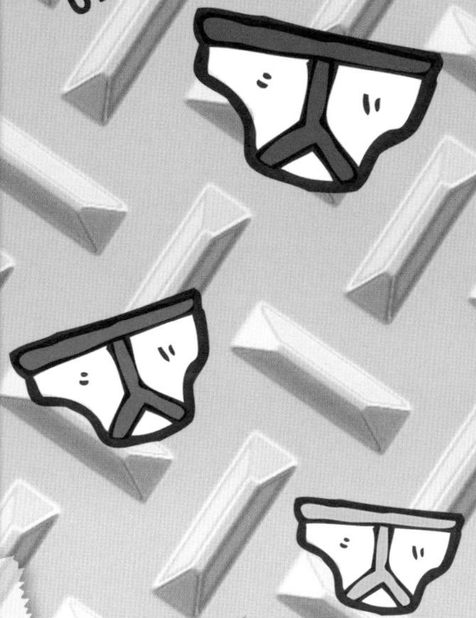

ROTTEN RATHERS!

Would you rather . . .

fill your pockets with cockroaches . . . or . . .
fill your shoes with maggots?

sit in a bathtub full of snakes . . . or . . .
dye your hair green?

run around school in your underwear . . . or . . .
have 6 months detention?

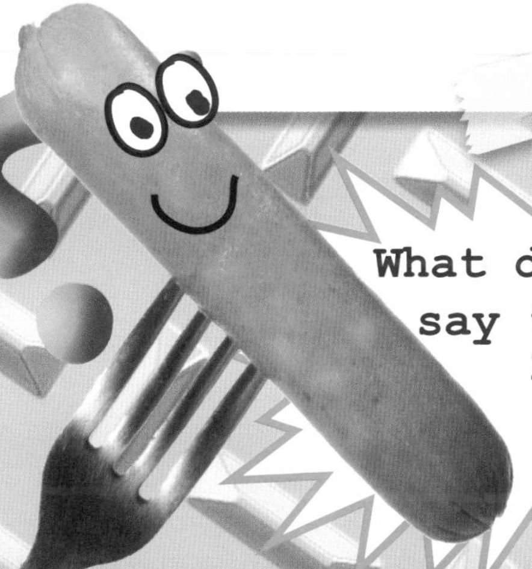

What did the sausage say to the bacon?
I HAM so pleased to MEAT you!

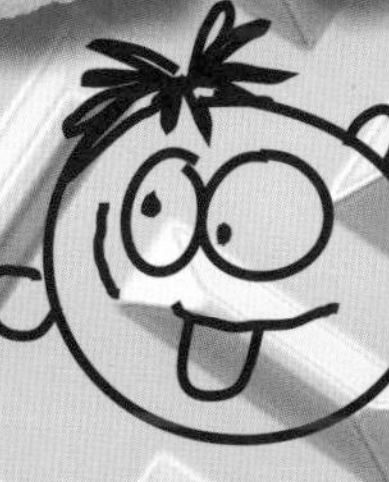

This is what I'd look like if I was a **pizza!**

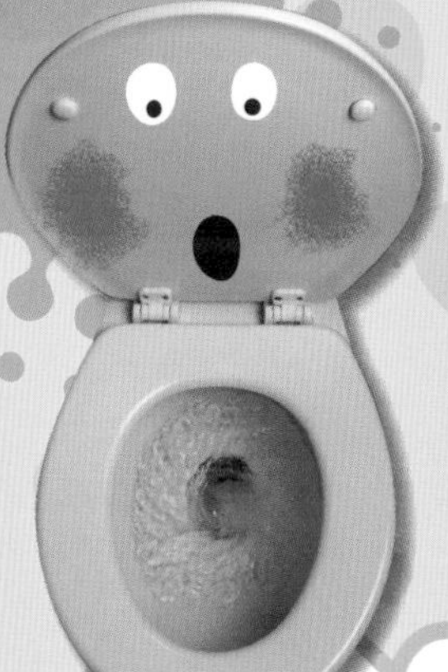

I'm too busy to...

Why couldn't the police solve the mystery of the missing toilet?

Because they had nothing to go on!

Famous people I'd like to prank!

1
2
3
4

My **5** best pranks!

1
2
3
4
5

Where's the best place to make a noise online?

The DIN-ternet

CRASH!

Mum wants me to . . .

People to prank today

1
2
3
4

Send your pals to sleep with one of the simplest pranks ever!

The next time you're with a group of friends or at a family party, see if you can set off a train of tiredness by simply yawning! Yawn just a little at first, then after a minute or two, yawn a little louder and longer. Watch to see if anyone else yawns, and then yawn some more! Before long, the rest of the room will be sent into a snooze!

YAWN!!!!!!!!!

Cut out this lovely spider and leave it on your sister's pillow!

What did the queen bee say when the worker bees started messing around?

Oh, do BEE-HIVE!

WHAT A PAIN!

CRAAAAAAACCK

Ever been told not to kick a ball in the house in case you BREAK A WINDOW? Prank your parents into believing you've done just that!

Take a piece of clingfilm and smooth it over a table or worktop. Using a black permanent marker, draw zigzag lines over the clingfilm. Now gently apply the film to a handy window, grab your ball and 'fess up!

TOP TIP

A window with lace curtains or a slatted blind will work best because they help hide creases in the clingfilm!

What do sea monsters eat at parties?

Ship 'n' dip!

ROTTEN RATHERS

Which would you choose? Write your names at the top and put a cross by your choices.

Names here

Cream pie in the face OR	☐	☐	☐	☐
mud pie in the face?	☐	☐	☐	☐
Sit in a bath of milk OR	☐	☐	☐	☐
sit in a bath of juice?	☐	☐	☐	☐
Worm sandwich OR	☐	☐	☐	☐
spider sandwich?	☐	☐	☐	☐

OR EEEK!

Stuff I'm going to do today!

Stuff I forgot to do yesterday!

Why didn't the snowman go to the disco?

Because he had tickets to the snow ball!

Today, I will not...

People to prank today

 1

 2

 3

 4

Why did the policeman stay in bed?

He wanted to work undercover!

PICK A PRANK NAME!

Every Prank Star needs a prank name – make yours here!

1 Take the first **three** letters of your **first name**. If the third letter is **NOT** a vowel (A, E, I, O, U), add an "a" and then simply add one of the following words:

bongo **bingo**
pongo **boogo**

2 Take the first **three** letters of your **last name**. If the third letter is **NOT** a vowel, add an "a" and then add on one of the following words:

bangsplat **badwiff**
boogerwort **navelfluff**

So if your name is **Alfie Sharrocks**, your prank name could be:

Alfabongo Shaboogerwort

THIS IS MY PRANK NAME!

- -

GIVE YOUR FRIENDS PRANK NAMES!

- -

now known as

- -

Metric MADNESS!

In 1975, an Australian news show announced that the country would be moving to "metric time". This meant that instead of 60 seconds, there would be 100 seconds in a minute and 100 minutes in an hour.

To make matters more crazy, there would be 20 hours in a day and seconds would be renamed "millidays" and hours "decidays".

They even showed a new clock with 10 hours on its face!

The salon called.

Hedda Hare

Meet you at the zoo.

Al E. Gaytor

Turn the music down!

Max E. Mumm

FUNNY FILLINGS!

Thrill your friends with some dreadful doughnuts!
Take two ring doughnuts and carefully make a hole in the bottom of one using the end of a teaspoon handle. Next, squirt a little mustard or tomato sauce on the end of the spoon handle and push it into the doughnut. Finally, put both doughnuts on a plate and offer one to a friend, being careful to take your doughnut first. Enjoy your sweet treat as your friend munches in misery!

HEE-HEE!

5+2+1

To do
(if I'm bored)

People to prank today

1
2
3
4

Why doesn't Tarzan need a calculator?
Because the jungle's full of adders!

Important! (ish)

DISGUSTING DIGIT!

Take a small foam or cardboard cup with a lid and make a hole big enough to stick your finger through. Put the middle finger of either hand through the hole and practise folding your fingers so it looks as though you are holding the cup in the palm of your hand. Put the lid on the cup and carry a book or bag in your other hand. Ask your brother to open the cup for you (because your hands are full) and as he opens the cup, wiggle your finger to give him the fright of his life!

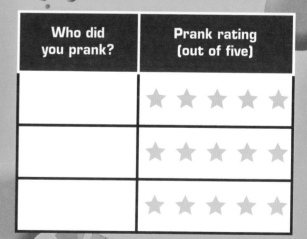

5 funniest people in the world

1.
2.
3.
4.
5.

IF I WAS AN **EGG**, I'D LOOK LIKE THIS . . .

Who did you prank?	Prank rating (out of five)
	★ ★ ★ ★ ★
	★ ★ ★ ★ ★
	★ ★ ★ ★ ★

HMMM?

Why did the woman put blusher on her forehead?
She was trying to make up her mind!

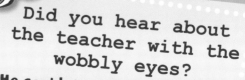

Did you hear about the teacher with the wobbly eyes?
He couldn't control his pupils!

WHAT'S THAT?!

A super-easy prank to get your friends staring.

All you do is stand still, then look up and point. Wait for a few seconds then lower your hand, walk on, and then look over your shoulder at the fools staring at the sky, wondering what you saw!

Great places to perform this prank include: **the park, at the zoo, a playground, the shopping mall or on a busy pavement!**

TOP TIP! Combine your pointing with a look of horror, joy or confusion to really get 'em looking!

TOILET TROUBLE PART 1

Make nature's call a moment to remember with this perfect prank!

Using a hole punch, make a generous handful of paper dots. When no one is looking, sneak into the bathroom and remove the roll of toilet paper.

Roll out about six sheets of toilet paper and scatter dots on the paper until you are two sheets from the end.

Next, carefully roll the paper back up and hook it on the toilet-roll holder. When your victim pulls at the roll, they'll find themselves showered in tiny dots!

Who did you prank?	Prank rating (out of five)
	★ ★ ★ ★ ★
	★ ★ ★ ★ ★
	★ ★ ★ ★ ★

To do!

5 most boring chores

 1

 2

 3

 4

5

Doctor, Doctor! How can I stop my nose running?

Tie its legs together!

To do!

To dodge!

A great prank to play on your brother or sister, but you'll need an adult to help.

Simply sew the corner of a handkerchief into the bottom of your victim's coat or trouser pocket. Wait for them to sneeze or need to blow their nose, and then laugh your pants off when they fail to pull the pesky rag from their pocket!

THAT'S *NOT* FUNNY!

Doodle arms, legs and hair on the sausages!

Why are scarves bad at sports?

They prefer to hang around!

THE **DO NOTHING** PRANK

Here's a way to punk your pals by doing absolutely NOTHING.

A couple of days before April 1st, tell your pal you've heard of some really amazing April 1st pranks. A little later, say you've thought up the most awesome prank ever, but refuse to share it. The next day, say you're just trying to decide who to pull the prank on. When it comes to April 1st, do nothing, but every time you see your pal smirk, look the other way or do anything to look suspicious – for example, keep looking at his bag in a way that suggests you put something in it or you are about to! All the while, do nothing – the prank is that your pal spent the day thinking he was about to be punk'd!

Cut out this moustache and become a master of disguise!

Things I'm not going to do today!

People to prank today

1
2
3
4

Which side of a bird has the most feathers?
The outside!

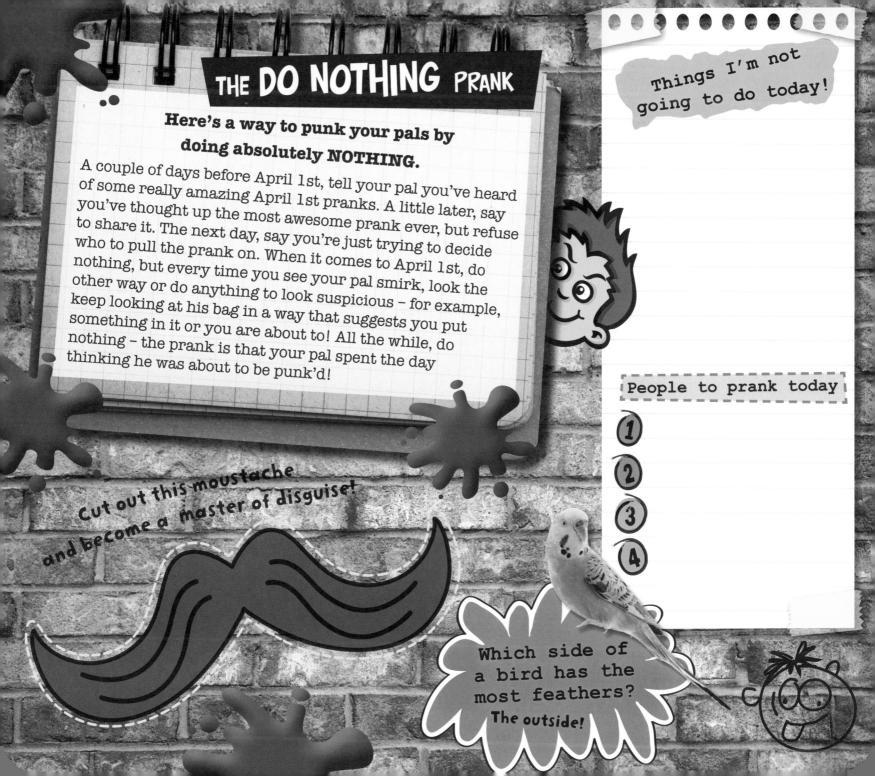

Things to do if I have time

People to prank today

1
2
3
4

If I was a tomato, I'd look like this. ↓

Where does a skunk wash his dishes?

In the kitchen STINK!

What did Mr. Volcano say to Mrs. Volcano when they got married?

I lava you!

THAT'S TORN IT!

This prank is almost too easy to be true and scores a straight A for maximum laughs at minimum effort!

Find an old piece of cloth and make small cuts around the edges – this will make the cloth easy to rip. Wait for a friend to bend over then swiftly rip the rag and delight in your pal thinking he's torn his trousers!

have triple geography homework . . . or . . .

play sports in your underpants?

have peanuts in your socks . . . or . . .

have jelly in your gloves?

drink sour milk . . . or . . .

eat wet toast?

OR

If I was a meatball, I'd look like this.

Don't forget

Things I'd like to do

MOVING MONEY!

Prank your pals as they make for the money!

Tape a coin to a long piece of black cotton and place it, tape down, on a table. Sit at the table with something light, like a piece of paper, covering the cotton trail and your hand underneath the table holding the end of the thread. Wait for your pal to join you at the table, and then the moment he makes a dash for the cash pull the cotton. Watch him jump out of his skin as the money escapes his greedy grasp!

What did the kettle say when the pan lost his temper?

Just SIMMER down!

Things to do before I'm too old

5 funniest movies ever!

1
2
3
4
5

DON'T DO THAT!

The best way to prank a pal into punking themselves is to tell them ABSOLUTELY not to do something!

If you say "don't", chances are the temptation will be just too much! The secret is to advise strongly against doing something really simple (like opening a book or cupboard) and then surprise them with a crazy consequence when the temptation becomes just too strong! Always leave your instruction on a large sticky note where it can't be missed! For example:

"Do NOT open page 52!" (Take any book and cover page 52 in hole-punch dots, then carefully close the book).

"This cupboard door must be kept CLOSED at all times!" (Hang plastic bugs and other freaky finds on the inside of the door frame.)

"Do not remove this newspaper!" (Sneak a splat of homemade puke under the paper for a sickening surprise!)

Achoo!

Doctor, Doctor, I caught a cold!

Then throw it back, you fool!

Who did you prank?	Prank rating (out of five)
	★ ★ ★ ★ ★
	★ ★ ★ ★ ★
	★ ★ ★ ★ ★

Did you hear about the plumber who couldn't mend pipes?
His business went down the drain!

Achoo!

Have you heard about the frog spy?

His name is Pond!

What are the fingers poking?

Things Mum wants me to do

Best Prank Stars in my family

SEW SNEAKY!

If you got endless joy from the Hilarious Hankies, go one step further and spring a morning surprise on your favourite brother or sister!

IMPORTANT! This prank definitely requires some grown-up help and permission!

While your victim is out of the house, raid their drawers for a nice selection of socks and underwear. With a needle and thread, carefully join them together with one or two stitches to create a chain of clothes, and then neatly place them back in the drawer.

The next morning, keep a joyful ear to their bedroom door as your bleary-eyed sibling reaches out and grabs a string of socks or a parade of underpants!

I might as well...

5 funniest teachers

1
2
3
4
5

SNOW JOKE

This is a classic prank – perfect for a rainy day!

- Find a hole punch and punch as many holes as you can before you get completely bored or your wrist aches.

- Find an umbrella and open it slightly.

- Pour the punched holes carefully into the umbrella and roll it back up, tightly.

- Wait for your victim to open up their umbrella, and then roll on the floor laughing when they are showered with tiny paper dots!

SHOWER YOUR FRIENDS WITH JOY!

Why was the hen banned from the Internet chatroom? Because her language was so fowl!

!!*!

Where's Timbuktu? Next to Timbukone!

Timbuktu

Timbukone

NO CONTROL!

Simply take the batteries out of the remote. So easy yet so effective. A nice prank to try right after the batteries have been replaced. For extra effect, replace the batteries with a message on a rolled up piece of paper – "Punk'd!" always goes down nicely.

Stuff I'm going to do **today**!

Stuff I forgot to do **yesterday**!

Give kitty a lovely moustache and glasses!

Who did you prank?	Prank rating (out of five)
	★ ★ ★ ★ ★
	★ ★ ★ ★ ★
	★ ★ ★ ★ ★

Where did the butterfly leave its dog?

Tied to the caterPILLAR!

Important!

Tell your pal he has an unsightly booger hanging from his nose. Keep telling him he hasn't quite got it as you watch him fish around his face!

Not important!

Who did you prank?	Prank rating (out of five)
	★ ★ ★ ★ ★
	★ ★ ★ ★ ★
	★ ★ ★ ★ ★

5 grossest things I've ever seen

1.
2.
3.
4.
5.

YAWN!

Why was the meatball tired?
Because it was pasta its bedtime!

MOVING MONUMENT!

In 1986, a French newspaper made the shocking – and totally untrue – announcement that the famous Eiffel Tower would be taken down and moved to become an attraction at the new Disney park in Paris!

OOH LA LA!

Give the fruit freaky faces!

Cool stuff!

Things to do

What did the curtains say to the window?

We've got you covered!

I will definitely...

People to prank

 1

 2

 3

 4

OR

There's nothing like being punk'd when you're minding your own business!

When no one is looking, take the roll of toilet paper from the bathroom. Replace it with a new roll until you are ready (so no one gets suspicious).

Unroll three sheets and put a few dots of glue on the third sheet. Roll it back up, press the glued area lightly and leave it to dry.

Once the glue is totally dry, roll the paper back up and put it in the holder with the first two sheets left dangling. Wait for your victim to answer nature's call, then listen to them wail when they fail to unravel the roll!

PARP!

ROTTEN RATHERS!

Would you rather . . .

speak backwards . . . or . . .

see upside down?

itch for six hours . . . or . . .

hiccup for three hours?

have ants in your pants . . . or . . .

spiders in your hair?

---

real life prank fact . . . real life prank fact . . .

Can Penguins Fly?

Of course they can't! But that didn't stop the BBC from airing a nature show in 2008 showing just that! The programme explained that, rather than put up with Antarctic winters, the perky penguins flew to the South American rainforests to enjoy the sun. Viewers were amazed to see the waddling wonders soaring through the sky – then later they were shown how it was done with special effects and camera trickery!

MILKY WAY!

This is a classic breakfast-time prank that always creates a stir! Simply add a few drops of green food colouring to a carton of milk, shake the carton gently, then place it on the table and let your family enjoy the sour-looking surprise!

YUCK!

SLIPPERY PENCILS!

Take a little liquid soap and smear it lightly over the barrels of two or three pencils. Place the pencils on a work surface and challenge a friend to a game of hangman. Offer them a pencil, and then join in the fun as they fail to get a grip!

If I don't forget, I'll...

People to prank

1
2
3
4

Why did the student study on a plane?

She wanted a higher education!

People who have pranked me

People to prank

1
2
3
4

Which famous sea creature never tidies its room?
The Loch Mess Monster!

Why was the whisk sent to jail?
It was beating the eggs!

Ouch!

MOVE-IT-AROUND MAYHEM!

This top gag is perfect to play on your sister or brother!

Sneak into your brother's or sister's room and simply move things around a little. For example, switch the books on the bookshelf so they are in a different order, rearrange the contents of their drawers, or move their favourite ornaments or trophies onto a different shelf. They may not notice the changes at first, but if they do, deny all knowledge and make a note to make some more changes the following day!

After two days, reveal your prank or the confusion may make them completely crazy!

MAGGOT ATTACK!

It's so simple to fool your parents into believing that their lovely fruit bowl has been invaded by insects!

Simply take an apple from the fruit bowl and make holes all around it using a sharp pencil. Leave the apple for a few hours and the holes will become nice and brown. Then return the fruit and scatter a few fake bugs around the bowl. Watch your mum howl in horror when she reaches for her favourite fruit!

If I was a peanut, I'd look like this!

No way will I do it

People to prank today

1
2
3
4

real life prank fact . . . real life prank fact . . .

Crazy colour

Years ago in Sweden, when all TV shows were shown in black and white, an expert announced that viewers could convert their TVs to colour by simply pulling an old nylon stocking over the screen! Seems some silly Swedes thought it was a great idea and were surprised when the stocking netted no results!

What's a cow's favourite film?

High School MOO-sical

Another cunning use of PVA glue – sure to delight friends and relatives alike!

You will need:

PVA glue an old magazine an old pencil
green paint clingfilm

Place the clingfilm on the magazine. Squirt a blob of glue on the clingfilm. Mix up a little green paint (or yellow, or both) and put a few drops on the glue blob. Use your pencil to mix the paint gently into the glue and create a nice booger shape. Leave to dry for at least a day. Gently peel the booger off the clingfilm.

Cut out the creepy crawlies and leave them lurking around the house!

Things I really want to do
(but probably won't)

People to prank today

1
2
3
4

What sound did the grape make when it got squashed?
A little wine!

5 excellent things to do with a
fake booger

(Note! Before pranking, make sure the paint will not rub off on anything!)

1 Leave it on top of your mum's lovely, fresh washing.

2 Place gently next to your sister's fork at the dinner table.

3 See if you can make it hang from your nose, and then go to school without it falling off.

4 Place it on the palm of your hand, then shake hands with a pal or random relative.

5 Stick one on the side of a packet of biscuits, then offer them to a favourite aunt.

SPRINGY SURPRISE!

Make opening a book a springy surprise!

Find a thick, OLD book – make sure it's one that no one wants. If it's not yours, ASK first! A hardback book is best for this prank.

Draw a circle about 3 cm in diameter in the middle of the first page and use this as a guide to cut a hole about 80 pages deep. Cut several pages at a time and use the hole you have cut to draw more cutting guides.

Next, cut a strip of cardboard about 15 cm long and 1 cm wide. Fold the cardboard back and forth every 1 cm to form a spring. Now cut a circle of cardboard just bigger than the hole. Draw something gross like a bug or an eyeball on the circle and stick it on the spring.

Fold the spring up, place it in the hole and carefully close the book. Hand the book to a friend, explaining that there is something completely fascinating on the first page. Point the book in their direction so they look down, and then open the cover quickly to give them a springy surprise!

ARGH!

POINNNG!

More prank notes to cut out and give.

Fancy a workout?
Jim Nasium

Can't wait for the party!

Felix Cited

Help! I can't get out!
Doris Shutt

Just get on and do it!

People to prank

---

real life prank fact . . . real life prank fact . . .

WHAT BARKING NONSENSE!

Animal Antics!

In 2010, Google took online pranking to a new level when it announced the "Translate for Animals" app. A special webpage announced that soon we'd be able to understand what our pets were saying with translators for dog-, chicken-, sheep- and even tortoise-talk available!

Did you hear about the angry woman who mistook her soap for cheese?
She was foaming at the mouth!

Things to get me in the good books!

People to prank today

1)

2)

3)

4)

YONKS! MY THUMB BROKE!

This classic gag fools 'em every time!

1) Bend the tops of both thumbs inwards as far as you can.

2) Place your thumbs together, so that the bottom half of one thumb joins with the top half of the other.

3) Wrap a forefinger around the "join" between the two thumbs.

4) Raise the top half of your new thumb slowly and stifle your smirks as your friends are fooled into believing that your thumb has broken in two!

TOP TIP! Practise different hand-finger combinations to perfect your prank!

OUCH!

ROTTEN RATHERS!

Would you rather . . .

pour a bucket of slugs over your head . . . or . . .

eat a snail sandwich?

have bananas for toes . . . or . . .

hotdogs for fingers?

Drink a glass of dirty bathwater . . . or . . .

drink a glass of pond water?

Why did the brainiac eat her homework?

Because it was a piece of cake!

TEE HEE!

What lives at the bottom of the sea and shakes?

A nervous wreck!

ALARMING!

There's nothing worse than being woken up when you are having a nice snooze, so why not give a "loved one" (that is, your older sister or younger brother) this treat by hiding an alarm clock in their room? Set the clock nice and early and hide it somewhere they wouldn't think to look. Be sure the clock hasn't got a loud tick or you may be rumbled!

IT'S ALL ABOUT TIMING!

To do!
(boo-hoo)

5 funniest TV shows

1
2
3
4
5

BEDTIME BEASTLINESS!

Give someone special a bedtime bonus!

Just before bedtime, sneak into your brother's or sister's room and pile some surprises under their sheets. Old shoes, for example, would make a fabulous find, as would a few crunchy cornflakes (be prepared to have to clean them up) or an old frying pan. Make the prank extra memorable by hiding the goodies UNDER the bottom sheet! Sweet dreams!

EEEEK!

Doctor, Doctor! I think I'm a yo-yo!

How do you feel?

Sometimes I'm up and sometimes I'm down!

How do you stop your dog from barking in the back of your car?

Put it in the front!

Oh, goody,
I've got to...

People to prank today

 1
 2
 3
 4

Why was the
computer
overweight?

It had too
many chips!

Why
couldn't
the frog
drive to
work?

Its car was
toad away!

SECRET CODES

If you want to be King of Pranks, you need to keep your secrets safe, and the best way is to create your own code.

Try using this back-to-front alphabet. Instead of A, you write Z, instead of B, you write Y, and so on.

A	B	C	D	E	F	G	H	I	J	K	L	M
Z	Y	X	W	V	U	T	S	R	Q	P	O	N

N	O	P	Q	R	S	T	U	V	W	X	Y	Z
M	L	K	J	I	H	G	F	E	D	C	B	A

Instead of letters you could use shapes, numbers or a mix of all three.

Try creating your own secret prank codes.

FREAKY FINGER

Tell your victim you've found something interesting on the pavement and ask them to open the box. LOL as your victim shrieks at the sight of your festering finger!

Find some cotton wool (enough to fill most of the box), dab it with dark red paint and leave it to dry.

Find a small gift box and cut a hole in the bottom large enough to stick your finger through.

Cup the box in your hand, placing your middle finger through the hole and pad the box with the cotton. Put the lid on the box.

Offer the box to your friends and wiggle your finger as they lift the lid!

ARGH!

WHAT'S COMING OUT OF THE ALIENS' NOSES?

Cool stuff to do

Boring stuff to do

STICKY PROBLEM

Get a tiny bit of honey and smear it on a bedroom door handle.

Sweet!

YUCK!

Who did you prank?	Prank rating (out of five)
	★ ★ ★ ★ ★
	★ ★ ★ ★ ★
	★ ★ ★ ★ ★

Do it!

Don't do it!

Cut out these prank notes and give them to someone special.

Set the alarm for six!

Earl E. Bird

Get off the couch!

Stan Dupp

PAPER PRANKING!

Take a slip of paper and write "Do Not Pull" on one end. Tape the paper into a magazine with the message peeking out of the side. Make lots of paper dots using a hole punch. Carefully fill the magazine with the paper dots. Place the magazine on a table. Watch and wait until someone is unable to resist yanking at the paper and sends a shower of paper dots into the air!

Who did you prank?	Prank rating (out of five)
	★ ★ ★ ★ ★
	★ ★ ★ ★ ★
	★ ★ ★ ★ ★

Why did the fool cut a hole in his umbrella?

So he could see when it stopped raining!

Where do astronauts keep their sandwiches?

In a launch box!

COOKIES 'N' SCREAM!

If filling a doughnut with a freaky flavour was just too much fun, try this biscuit-based caper for a load more laughs!

Take a selection of sandwich-style biscuits and gently open them up. Add an edible (but unexpected) flavour to the cream filling — for example a sprinkling of salt and pepper or a little mustard — then carefully put the biscuits back together. Offer your friends a tasty treat then watch their faces fall as they sample the terrible taste!

No, I will not!

People to prank

1
2
3
4
5

If I was a fish, I'd look like this!

What colour are hiccups?

BURPLE!

How does the sea wear its hair?

Wavy!

To do!

To dodge!

Hothead!

In 1995, a magazine called *Discover* claimed that a new species had been discovered in Antarctica. The brainy boffins told their readers that this fearsome creature had bones on its head that could become red hot, helping it to cut through snow and ice while chasing penguins! This hot news was, of course, nothing but nonsense!

ROTTEN RATHERS!

Would you rather . . .

swim near jellyfish . . . **or . . .**

ski blindfolded?

drink a ketchup milkshake. . . **or . . .**

eat mayonnaise on ice cream?

have caterpillar eyebrows . . . **or . . .**

have spaghetti hair?

How do fishermen catch virtual fish?

On line!

Why was the skeleton feeling lonely?

Because he had **NO BODY** to play with!